21ST CENTURY HITS
Playalong *for* Flute

G000054901

Wise Publications
part of The Music Sales Group
London/New York/Paris/Sydney/Copenhagen/Berlin/Madrid/Tokyo

Published by
Wise Publications
14-15 Berners Street, London W1T 3LJ, UK.

Exclusive Distributors:
Music Sales Limited
Distribution Centre, Newmarket Road, Bury St Edmunds,
Suffolk IP33 3YB, UK.
Music Sales Pty Limited
120 Rothschild Avenue, Rosebery, NSW 2018, Australia.

Order No. AM992772
ISBN 13: 978-1-84772-458-8
This book © Copyright 2008 Wise Publications,
a division of Music Sales Limited.

Arranging and engraving supplied by Camden Music.
Edited by Sam Harrop.
Compiled by Nick Crispin.

Printed in the EU.

CD recorded, mixed and mastered by Jonas Persson.
Flute played by John Whelan.

Your Guarantee of Quality:
As publishers, we strive to produce every book to
the highest commercial standards.
The music has been freshly engraved and the book has been
carefully designed to minimise awkward page turns and
to make playing from it a real pleasure.
Particular care has been given to specifying acid-free, neutral-sized
paper made from pulps which have not been elemental chlorine bleached.
This pulp is from farmed sustainable forests and was
produced with special regard for the environment.
Throughout, the printing and binding have been planned to
ensure a sturdy, attractive publication which should give years of enjoyment.
If your copy fails to meet our high standards,
please inform us and we will gladly replace it.

www.musicsales.com

Flute Fingering Chart

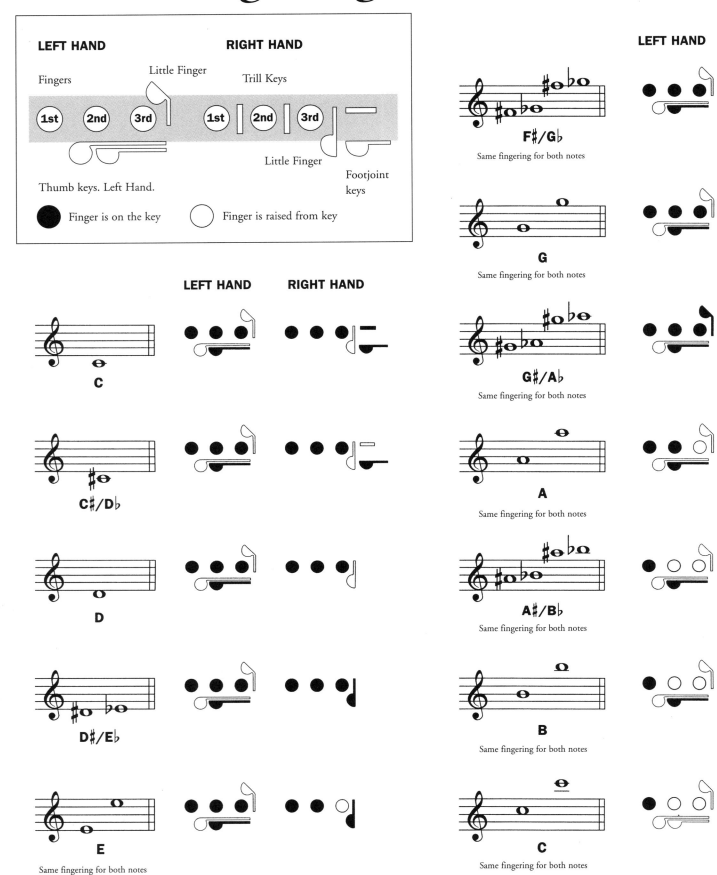

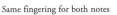

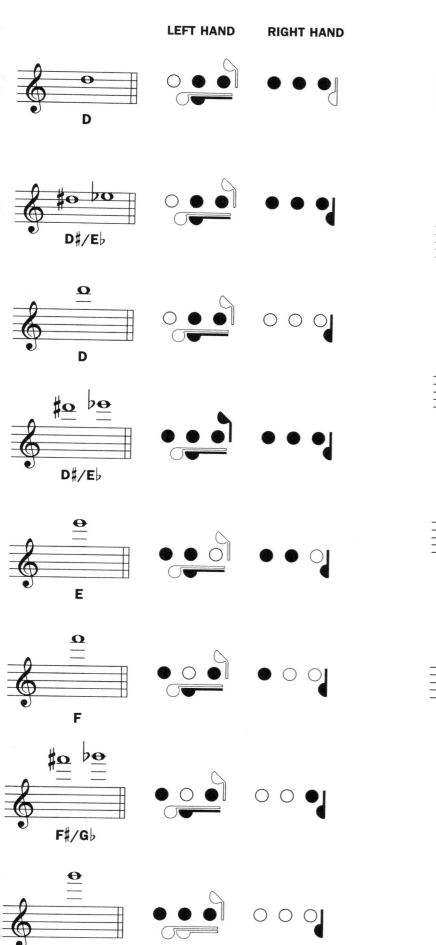

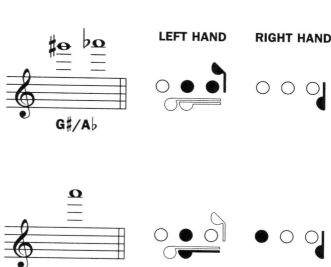

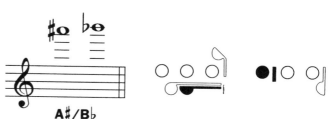

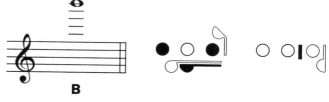

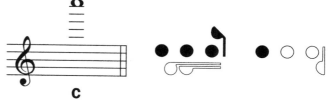

All About You (McFly)

Words & Music by Thomas Fletcher

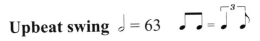

violin cue (8va)

rubato   A tempo

Much slower, rubato

Beautiful Day (U2)

Words by Bono
Music by U2

Don't Know Why (Norah Jones)

Words & Music by Jesse Harris

Everytime (Britney Spears)

Words & Music by Britney Spears & Annette Stamatelatos

I Don't Feel Like Dancin' (Scissor Sisters)

Words & Music by Elton John, Jason Sellards & Scott Hoffman

Disco Rock ♩ = 108

f sempre

1973 (James Blunt)

Words & Music by Mark Batson & James Blunt

Fade to end

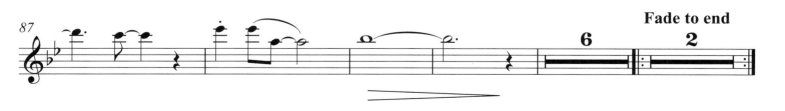

Other Side Of The World (KT Tunstall)

Words & Music by KT Tunstall & Martin Terefe

Steadily ♩ = 80

electric piano cue

Patience (Take That)

Words & Music by Mark Owen, Gary Barlow, John Shanks, Jason Orange & Howard Donald

Moderate pop ballad ♩ = 88

cresc. poco a poco

Put Your Records On (Corinne Bailey Rae)

Words & Music by John Beck, Steven Chrisanthou & Corinne Bailey Rae

You Raise Me Up (Westlife)

Words & Music by Rolf Lovland & Brendan Graham

CD Track Listing

1. Tuning notes

Full instrumental performances...

2. All About You
(Fletcher) Universal Music Publishing Limited.

3. Beautiful Day
(Hewson/Evans/Mullen/Clayton) Blue Mountain Music Limited.

4. Don't Know Why
(Harris) Sony/ATV Music Publishing (UK) Limited.

5. Everytime
(Spears/Stamatelatos)
Universal Music Publishing Limited/Notting Hill Music Limited/Zomba Music Publishing Limited.

6. I Don't Feel Like Dancin'
(John/Sellards/Hoffman) EMI Music Publishing Limited/Universal Music Publishing Limited.

7. 1973
(Blount/Batson) EMI Music Publishing Limited/Universal/MCA Music Limited.

8. Other Side Of The World
(Tunstall) Sony/ATV Music Publishing (UK) Limited.

9. Patience
(Barlow/Orange/Owen/Donald/Shanks)
Sony/ATV Music Publishing (UK) Limited/EMI Music Publishing Limited/
Warner/Chappell North America/Universal Music Publishing MGB Limited.

10. Put Your Records On
(Bailey Rae/Beck/Chrisanthou) Good Groove Songs Limited/Global Talent Publishing.

11. You Raise Me Up
(Graham/Lovland) Peermusic (UK) Limited/Universal Music Publishing Limited.

Backing tracks only...

12. All About You

13. Beautiful Day

14. Don't Know Why

15. Everytime

16. I Don't Feel Like Dancin'

17. 1973

18. Other Side Of The World

19. Patience

20. Put Your Records On

21. You Raise Me Up

To remove your CD from the plastic sleeve,
lift the small lip to break the perforations.
Replace the disc after use for convenient storage.